Published 2013 by
A & C Black, an imprint of Bloomsbury Publishing Plc
50 Bedford Square, London, WC1B 3DP
www.bloomsbury.com
www.poetryzone.co.uk

ISBN 978-1-4081-9294-8

A CIP catalogue for this book is available from the British Library.

Printed and bound by CPI Group (UK) Ltd, Croydon CR0 4YY

1 3 5 7 9 10 8 6 4 2

Off By Heart

Roger Stevens
illustrated by Spike Gerrell

A & C BLACK
AN IMPRINT OF BLOOMSBURY
LONDON NEW DELHI NEW YORK SYDNEY

Contents

Note

The poems in this book are arranged in order of length. The number in the top corner of each page tells you how many lines each poem has.

A Poem That, Despite Being Only One Word Long, Can Sometimes Make a Crowd be Quiet and can be Easily Understood by a Baby

Shhhhh…

Roger Stevens

Although this poem is only one word long, you do have to learn and say the title too!

2

Visiting the Library

Look!
Book!

Josephine Bodsworth

2

What's the Difference?

A dog is like a puppy...
just a little more grown-uppy!

Graham Denton

11

2

The Witch! The Witch!

The Witch! The Witch! Don't let her get you!
Or your aunt wouldn't know you the next time she
  met you!

Eleanor Farjeon

Feeling Sniffy

Dandelion seeds are flying
free upon the breeze.
They're so pretty, it's a pity
that they make me sneeze!

Matt Goodfellow

4

Revenge

My brother chased me with a crab,
He found it by a rock,
But I will get my own back –
It's now inside his sock!

Coral Rumble

An Autumn Greeting

"Come," said the wind to the leaves one day.
"Come over the meadow and we will play.
Put on your dresses of red and gold.
For summer is gone and the days grow cold."

Anon

4

The Fly

Buzz buzz, buzz buzz
Buzz buzz, buzz buzz
Buzz buzz, buzz buzz
SPLAT!

Andy Croft

The Old Man of Blackheath

There was an old man of Blackheath,
Who sat on a set of false teeth;
He said, with a start,
"Oh Lord, bless my heart,
I have bitten myself underneath."

Anon

17

5

Owl

An owl was heard to remark,
"I'd much rather rise with the lark;
All this reading at night
Isn't good for my sight,
And, besides which, I'm scared of the dark!"

Graham Denton

Old Doctor MacDonald

There's an animal doctor in Slough
Who can comfort a dog in Bow-wow,
He can soothe too in Moo,
Gobble, Chirrup, Baa, Coo,
Hee haw, Cluck, Quack, Grunt, Squeak and Meow.

Philip Waddell

6

Hey Diddle Diddle

Hey diddle diddle
The cat and the fiddle
The cow jumped over the bed
The little dog laughed
But not for long
'Cos the cow landed right on his head

Roger Stevens

At the Zoo

First I saw the white bear, then I saw the black;
Then I saw the camel with a hump upon his back;
Then I saw the grey wolf, with mutton in his maw;
Then I saw the wombat waddle in the straw;
Then I saw the elephant a-waving of his trunk;
Then I saw the monkeys—mercy, how unpleasantly
    they smelt!

William Makepeace Thackeray

21

7

Puddle Muddle

My brother's in a muddle
'cause he sat down in a puddle
and he cried for his Mum, Mum, Mum.
I pulled him from the puddle
and gave him such a cuddle
that he sat back down right on his

...bottom.

Judith Nicholls

The Crocodile's Brushing His Teeth

The Crocodile's brushing his teeth, I'm afraid
This certainly means we're too late.
The Crocodile's brushing his teeth, I'm afraid
He has definitely put on some weight.
The Crocodile's brushing his teeth, I'm afraid
It really is, oh, such a bore.
The Crocodile's brushing his teeth, I'm afraid
He appears to have eaten class four!

Colin McNaughton

8

Animal Sneezes

A dog sneezes
atishoo!
An ant sneezes
atishoo!
A frog sneezes
a tish oo!
An elephant sneezes

ATISHOO!

Roger Stevens

Anything

Anything that's broken
I will mend

Anything that needs to go
I will send

Anytime you call me
I shall attend

You can ask me anything
I am your friend

Bernard Young

8

The Eccentric

He kept six butterflies chained in the yard
Oh, what an afternoon

He fed them on beer, tin-tacks and lard
Oh, what an afternoon

He powdered his hair with pumpkin squash
And sent his dirty teeth to the wash,

Oh what a, oh what a, oh what a, oh what a,
Oh, what an afternoon!

Anon

John Wesley

There was a man, he had two sons,
And these two sons were brothers.
John Wesley was the name of one,
And Charlie was the other's.

Now these two brothers had a coat,
They bought it on a Monday.
John Wesley wore it all the week,
And Charlie on a Sunday.

Anon

27

8

Baby Seeds

In a milkweed cradle
Snug and warm,
Baby seeds are hiding
Safe from harm.
Open wide the cradle,
Hold it high!
Come Mr Wind,
Help them fly.

Anon

My Sari

Saris hang on the washing line:
a rainbow in our neighbourhood.
This little orange one is mine,
it has a mango leaf design.
I wear it as a Rani would.
It wraps around me like sunshine,
it ripples silky down my spine,
and I stand tall and feel so good.

Debjani Chatterjee

8

Flint

An emerald is as green as grass,
A ruby red as blood;
A sapphire shines as blue as heaven;
A flint lies in the mud.
A diamond is a brilliant stone,
To catch the world's desire;
An opal holds a fiery spark;
But a flint holds fire.

Christina Rossetti

The Crocodile

How doth the little crocodile
Improve his shining tail,
And pour the waters of the Nile
On every golden scale!

How cheerfully he seems to grin
How neatly spreads his claws,
And welcomes little fishes in,
With gently smiling jaws!

Lewis Carroll

8

Weave Me a Poem

Weave me a poem of ribbons and strings.
Hatch me a poem of feathers and wings.
Grow me a poem of sunlight and soil.
Paint me a poem of canvas and oil.

Build me a poem of timber and stone.
Dance me a poem of muscle and bone.
Bake me a poem of sugar and cream.
Sing me a poem. I'm ready to dream.

Eric Ode

The Dragonfly

When the heat of summer
Made drowsy the land,
A dragonfly came
And sat on my hand,
With its blue jointed body,
And wings like spun glass,
It lit on my fingers
As though they were grass.

Eleanor Farjeon

8

I Went to the Animal Fair

I went to the animal fair
The birds and beasts were there
By the light of the moon the big baboon
Was combing his golden hair
The monkey fell out of his bunk
And slid down the elephant's trunk
The elephant sneezed and fell on his knees
But what became of the monkey, monkey, monkey,
    monkey...

Anon

This poem works well performed by two groups. The first group says the poem. At the end they keep repeating monkey monkey monkey monkey *whilst the second group says the poem. When the second group reach the end they keep repeating the word* monkey *whilst the first group then says the poem. This carries on until everyone has had enough or the teacher goes barmy!*

10

My Puppy

My puppy is so naughty
He always runs away
He never hears me when I call
Or stops when I say STAY!

My puppy only listens
And stops tearing down the street
When he hears his favourite word
TREAT!

TREAT!!

TREAT!!!

Debra Bertulis

Caterpillar

Brown and furry
Caterpillar in a hurry,
Take your walk
To the shady leaf, or stalk,
Or what not,
Which may be the chosen spot.
No toad spy you,
Hovering bird of prey pass by you;
Spin and die,
To live again a butterfly.

Christina Rossetti

10

Answer to a Child's Question

Do you ask what the birds say? The sparrow, the dove,
The linnet and thrush say, "I love and I love!"
In the winter they're silent – the wind is so strong;
What it says, I don't know, but it sings a loud song.
But green leaves, and blossoms, and sunny warm weather,
And singing, and loving – all come back together.
But the lark is so brimful of gladness and love,
The green fields below him, the blue sky above,
That he sings, and he sings; and for ever sings he –
"I love my Love, and my Love loves me!"

Samuel Taylor Coleridge

The Butter Betty Bought

Betty Botta bought some butter;
"But," said she, "this butter's bitter!
If I put it in my batter
It will make my batter bitter.
But a bit o' better butter
Will but make my batter better."
Then she bought a bit o' butter
Better than the bitter butter,
Made her bitter batter better.
So 'twas better Betty Botta
Bought a bit o' better butter.

Carolyn Wells

A tricky one…

12

Chicken Soup

Hear the soup
Bubble

Smell the soup
Yum

See the soup
Cook

Touch the bowl
Hot

Taste the soup
Yuk!

I never did like
Chicken soup

Roger Stevens

Like Grandad

Grandad's dog
has chubby little legs.

Like Grandad.

His eyes are sharp
and brown and bright.

Like Grandad.

When he's asleep
he snores and snorts.

Like Grandad.

He loves me and
I love him.

Like Grandad.

Joan Poulson

12

Gingerbread Man

Gingerbread's too hard,
Said the Gingerbread Man,
I'd rather be made of marzipan.

Marzipan's too soft,
Said the Marzipan Man,
I'd rather be made of strawberry jam.

Strawberry jam's too runny,
Said the Strawberry Jam Man,
I'd rather be made of plain meringue.

Meringue's too stiff,
The Meringue Man said,
I'd rather be made of gingerbread!

Celia Warren

Bumpety, Bumpety, Bump!

A farmer went trotting upon his grey mare
Bumpety, bumpety, bump!
With his daughter behind him so rosy and fair
Lumpety, lumpety, lump!

A raven cried, Croak! And they all tumbled down,
Bumpety, bumpety, bump!
The mare broke her knees and the farmer his crown
Lumpety, lumpety, lump!

The mischievous raven flew laughing away
Bumpety, bumpety, bump!
And vowed he would serve them the same the next day,
Lumpety, lumpety, lump!

Anon

12

A Silver Birch

A silver birch
Grows on the hill
All is calm
All is still

A flash of grey
The leaves all dance
A squirrel jumps
From branch to branch

A silver birch
Grows on the hill
The squirrel's gone
And all is still

Roger Stevens

Eletelephony

Once there was an elephant
Who tried to use the telephant.
No! No! I mean an elephone
Who tried to use the telephone.

(Dear me! I am not certain quite
That even now I've got it right.)
Howe'er it was, he got his trunk
Entangled in the telephunk.

The more he tried to get it free,
The louder buzzed the telephee.
(I fear I'd better drop the song
Of elephop and telephong!)

Laura Elizabeth Richards

12

The Moon

The moon has a face like the clock in the hall;
She shines on thieves on the garden wall.
On streets and fields and harbour quays,
And birdies asleep in the forks of trees.

The squalling cat and the squeaking mouse,
The howling dog by the door of the house,
The bat that lies in bed at noon,
All love to be out by the light of the moon.

But all of the things that belong to the day
Cuddle to sleep to be out of her way;
And flowers and children close their eyes
Till up in the morning the sun shall arise.

Robert Louis Stevenson

Ways to Come to School

George comes to school in a sports car
Mel comes to school on the bus

Will comes to school on his scooter
(So does Arthur and Sandy and Gus)

Billy comes to school on a snail
That's why he's always late

Miss Moss comes to school in the Tardis
She says Doctor Who's her best mate

Mr Walton arrives on a dragon
It's his very special pet

But I'm always the first to arrive at school
In my supersonic jet

(Although usually I walk…)

Roger Stevens

13

Doggerel

Dog thought up a poem.
Dog barked the poem.
The Moon thought it was cool.

Dog thought up a poem.
Dog barked the poem.
The Sun warmed to it.

Dog thought up a poem.
Dog barked the poem.
The Stars came out to listen.

Dog thought up a poem.
Dog barked the poem.
Dog barked it loud.

Cat Critic was not impressed.

Alan Murphy

When I Swing

When I swing
I seem
to forget
everything
I wash
my mind
in the sky.
Feet first
I burst
this blur
of world
and

fly
fly
fly.

Matt Goodfellow

15

Emergencies

Red Alert! Red Alert!
I've dropped my lolly in the dirt.

S.O.S! S.O.S!
I've spilled some custard
Down my dress.

999! 999!
My bike's got tangled
In the washing line.

Ring the alarm! Ring the alarm!
There's an insect landing
On my arm.

Bring First Aid! Bring First Aid!
There's a beetle in my lemonade.

Ambulance! And make it quick!
I think I'm going to be sick.

Tony Mitton

Big Red Boots

Big red boots, big red boots.
One of them squeaks and the other one toots.
One of them hops and the other one stamps.
Big red boots take long, wet tramps.

Boots, boots, big red boots.
One of them squeaks and the other one toots.

Big red boots on busy little feet
Start out shiny, clean and neat.
Big red boots, oh, yes, yes, yes,
End up muddy in a terrible mess.

Boots, boots, big red boots.
One of them squeaks and the other one toots.

Big red boots, big red boots,
Squelch through mud and trample roots.
Big red boots say, "Look! Oh gosh!
What a great puddle there... Yay! SPLOSH!"

Tony Mitton

16

What is Pink?

What is pink? A rose is pink
By the fountain's brink.
What is red? A poppy's red
In its barley bed.
What is blue? The sky is blue
Where the clouds float thro'
What is white? A swan is white
Sailing in the light.
What is yellow? Pears are yellow,
Rich and ripe and mellow.
What is green? The grass is green.
With small flowers between.
What is violet? Clouds are violet
In the summer twilight.
What is orange? Why, an orange,
Just an orange!

Christina Rossetti

The Rooks

The rooks are building on the trees;
They build there every spring:
"Caw, caw," is all they say,
For none of them can sing.
They're up before the break of day,
And up till late at night;
For they must labour busily
As long as it is light.
And many a crooked stick they bring,
And many a slender twig,
And many a tuft of moss, until
Their nests are round and big.
"Caw, caw." Oh, what a noise
They make in rainy weather!
Good children always speak by turns,
But rooks all talk together.

Jane Euphemia Browne

17

Performing Monkey

I'm not a performing monkey
I don't live in the zoo
I'm not a performing monkey
I don't go OO! OO! OO!

I'm not a performing monkey
I don't swing in a tree
I'm not a performing monkey
I don't go OO-EE-EEH!

I'm not a performing monkey
I'm not a go-rill-a
I'm not a performing monkey
I don't go OO-AH-AH!

I'm not a performing monkey
I don't live in the zoo
But as a special treat
I'll say this poem
Just for you!

Joshua Seigal

18

Snow

White snow,
bright snow,
silent in the night snow.
Crystal petal
snowflakes settle.
Sparkle in the light snow.

Deep snow,
heaped snow,
leap about and sweep snow.
Snowmen, snowballs,
snowdrifts, snowfalls.
Hands and feet aglow snow.

Cold snow,
old snow,
melting as you hold snow.
Icy, slushy,
dirty, mushy...
Time for you to go, snow.

Jane Clarke

19

Fat Cat

Our cat, Scampi,
Is a greedy cat,
And he gets fatter every day.

On Monday he squeezes
Through the cat flap.

On Tuesday he squeeeeezes
Through the cat flap.

On Wednesday he squeeeeeezes
Through the cat flap.

On Thursday he squeeeeeeeeezes
Through the cat flap.

On Friday he squeeeeeeeeeeezes
Through the cat flap.

On Saturday he squeeeeeeeeeeeeezes
Through the cat flap.

On Sunday he sqeeeeee
He sqeeeeee
He squeeeeeeeeeeee

On Sunday he stays outside!

Roger Stevens

19

Chocolate in the House

There's chocolate in the house,
I hear it calling me.
There's chocolate in the house,
I can't stay away.
There's chocolate in the house,
It's drawing me near.
There's chocolate in the house,
To resist is useless.
There's chocolate in the house,
I'll just go and see what kind it is.
There's chocolate in the house,
It's a good kind.
There's chocolate in the house,
I'll just try a bit.
There's chocolate in the house,
Mmmmm...
There's chocolate in the house
Smooth and creamy...

There's no chocolate in the house.

Andy Seed

I Am a Princess

Hello.
I am pleased to meet you
I am a princess
And I have a lot of rules
Which you must obey

Whenever you see me
You must bow or curtsey
You must never argue with me

Because a princess is always right

You must never wear a dress
That is prettier than mine

I choose the game we will play
And it is always my turn first

Remember. You are very lucky
To be playing with me.

And I have to win every game.

But before you go
Could you please explain
Why I have no friends?

Roger Stevens

20

Ladybird

Ladybird, Ladybird,
so tiny and bright,
I wonder, I wonder,
where you sleep at night.

Ladybird, Ladybird,
so easily seen,
I wonder, I wonder,
why red and not green.

Ladybird, Ladybird,
at home in the sky,
I wonder, I wonder,
when you learnt to fly.

Ladybird, Ladybird,
when Winter draws near,
I wonder, I wonder,
why you disappear.

Ladybird, Ladybird,
in so many ways, you're
a wonder, a wonder,
that brightens my days.

Brian D'Arcy

20

The Cats' Party

What a noise last night upon my roof!
What a NOISE last night upon my ROOF!
WHAT A NOISE LAST NIGHT UPON MY ROOF –
As the cats all had a party!

They sang miaow and their claws went scratch!
They sang MIAOW and their claws went SCRATCH!
THEY SANG MIAOW AND THEIR CLAWS WENT
  SCRATCH –
As the cats all had a party!

The Ginger Tom did a backward flip!
The GINGER TOM did a BACKWARD FLIP!
THE GINGER TOM DID A BACKWARD FLIP –
As the cats all had a party!

The Persian Blue had a purr-fect time!
The PERSIAN BLUE had a PURR-FECT time!
THE PERSIAN BLUE HAD A PURR-FECT TIME –
As the cats all had a party!

I tried to sleep but I stayed awake!
I tried to SLEEP but I STAYED AWAKE!
I TRIED TO SLEEP BUT I STAYED AWAKE –
As the cats all had a party!

Trevor Harvey

At the end of lines 1, 2 and 3...
in verse 1: cover both ears with your hands
in verse 2: scratch at the air with the fingers of your
right hand
in verse 3: trace a large circle in the air in front of you
with your right hand
in verse 4: move both hands outwards, in opposite
directions, on 'purr'
in verse 5: stretch your arms in the air and yawn

20

Don't Be Such a Fusspot

Don't be such a fusspot,
an always-in-a-rushpot.

Don't be such a weepypot,
a sneak-to-mum-and-be-creepypot.

Don't be such a muddlepot,
a double-dose-of-troublepot.

Don't be such a wigglepot,
a sit-on-your-seat-don't-squigglepot.

Don't be such a muckypot,
a pick-up-slugs-and-be-yuckypot.

Don't be such a sleepypot,
a beneath-the-bedclothes-peepypot.

Don't be such a fiddlepot,
a mess-about-and-meddlepot.

Don't be such a bossypot,
a saucypot, a gigglepot.

Don't be such a lazypot,
a nigglepot, a slackpot.

And don't call me a crackpot...
Who do you think you are?

Brian Moses

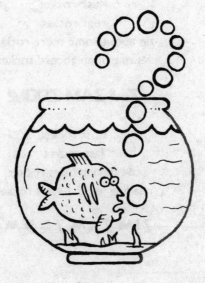

20

Zim Zam Zoom!

Brown rocket
green rocket
first I've seen rocket
best there's ever been rocket

ZIM ZAM ZOOM!

Rush rocket
roar rocket
zip about some more rocket
let me climb aboard rocket

ZIM ZAM ZOOM!

Blast rocket
fast rocket
overtaking Mars rocket
heading for the stars rocket

ZIM ZAM ZOOM!

Red rocket
blue rocket
racing to the moon rocket
won't you come back soon rocket

ZIM ZAM ZOOM!

James Carter

22

Mrs Sprockett's Strange Machine

Mrs Sprockett has a strange machine
It will thrill you through and through
It's got wheels and springs and seven strings
And this is what they do.

Pull string number one…
…it begins to hum mmmmmmmmmmmmm

Pull string number two…
…it goes COCK A DOODLE DOO.

Pull string number three…
…it will buzz like a bee zzzzzzzzzzzzzzzzzzzzzzzz

Pull string number four…
…it will start to ROAR.

Pull string number five…
…it will dip and dive.

Pull string number six…
…it will play silly tricks.

Pull string number seven…
…it will fly up to heaven.

Mrs Sprockett has a strange machine
It will thrill you through and through
It's got wheels and springs and seven strings
And… I WISH I HAD ONE TOO!

Michaela Morgan

22

There Are No Such Things as Monsters!!!

There's no such thing as the TOAST MONSTER
Who lives on crumbs and bread

There's no such thing as the FLUFF MONSTER
Who lives underneath your bed

There's no such thing as the U-BEND MONSTER
Who lives beneath the sink

There's no such things as the FRIDGE MONSTER
Who jumps out when you need a drink

There's no such thing as the WARDROBE MONSTER
Who comes out to play when it's dark

There's no such thing as the LOST BALL MONSTER
Who eats lost balls in the park

There's no such thing as the VACUUM CLEANER
  MONSTER
Who lives under the stairs

There's no such thing as the TOY BOX MONSTER
Who scares your teddy bears

There's no such thing as the TOILET MONSTER
Who lives inside the loo

There's no such thing as monsters.
And there's NOT one behind you.

Look!

BOO!!!

Roger Stevens

22

Pirate Hat

I wish I had
A pirate hat, a pirate hat
A pirate hat
I wish I had a pirate hat
Like my brother Jack's.

So I said, Jack
Will you swap your hat
For a football? For a football?
Will you swap your hat
For a football?
Jack said, Yes,
Let's do that.

And now I have a pirate hat
A pirate hat, a pirate hat
And now I have a pirate hat
What can be better that that?

But now the holidays are over
And my mates have all come back
Now I wish I had a football
A football, a football
I wish I had a football
Like my brother Jack.

Roger Stevens

24

Whisper, Whisper

whisper whisper
whisper whisper
goes my sister
down the phone

whisper whisper
go the beech leaves
breathing in
the wind alone

whisper whisper
whisper whisper
slips the river
on the stone

whisper whisper
go my parents
when they whisper
on their own

I don't mind
the whisper whisper
whisper whisper
it's a tune

sometimes though
I wish the whisper
whisperings would
shut up soon

Kit Wright

75

24

My Little Pet Cattery

My little pet
cattery
was very big and
fattery
he wore a little
hattery
because his head was
flattery.

One day my little
cattery
dived headlong in a
vattery,
he spluttered and he
spattery
but by then it didn't
mattery.

Now my little
cattery
in his basket he is
sattery;
his heart beats
pitter-pattery
because he's fitted with a
battery.

John Rice

24

The Chickens

Said the first little chicken
With a funny little squirm,
"I wish I could find
A fat little worm."
Said the next little chicken
With an odd little shrug,
"I wish I could find
A fat little slug."
Said the third little chicken,
With a sharp little squeal,
"I wish I could find
Some nice yellow meal."
Said the fourth little chicken,
With a small sigh of grief,
"I wish I could find
A little green leaf."
Said the fifth little chicken,
With a faint little moan,
"I wish I could find
A wee gravel stone."

"Now see here," said the mother,
From the green garden patch,
"If you want any breakfast
Just come here and scratch."

Anon

24

Little Raindrops

Oh, where do you come from,
You little drops of rain,
Pitter patter, pitter patter,
Down the window pane?

They won't let me walk,
And they won't let me play,
And they won't let me go
Out of doors at all today.

They put away my playthings
Because I broke them all,
And then they locked up all my bricks,
And took away my ball.

Tell me, little raindrops,
Is that the way you play,
Pitter patter, pitter patter,
All the rainy day?

They say I'm very naughty,
But I've nothing else to do
But sit here at the window;
I should like to play with you.

The little raindrops cannot speak,
But "pitter pitter pat"
Means, "We can play on this side,
Why can't you play on that?"

Jane Euphemia Browne

24

The Garden Year

January brings the snow,
Makes our feet and fingers glow.

February brings the rain,
Thaws the frozen lake again.

March brings breezes, loud and shrill,
To stir the dancing daffodil.

April brings the primrose sweet,
Scatters daisies at our feet.

May brings flocks of pretty lambs
Skipping by their fleecy dams.

June brings tulips, lilies, roses,
Fills the children's hands with posies.

Hot July brings cooling showers,
Apricots and gillyflowers.

August brings the sheaves of corn,
Then the harvest home is borne.

Warm September brings the fruit;
Sportsmen then begin to shoot.

Fresh October brings the pheasant;
Then to gather nuts is pleasant.

Dull November brings the blast;
Then the leaves are whirling fast.

Chill December brings the sleet,
Blazing fire and Christmas treat.

Sara Coleridge

25

The Way Through the Woods

They shut the road through the woods
Seventy years ago.
Weather and rain have undone it again,
And now you would never know
There was once a road through the woods
Before they planted the trees.
It is underneath the coppice and heath,
And the thin anemones.
Only the keeper sees
That, where the ring-dove broods,
And the badgers roll at ease,
There was once a road through the woods.

Yet, if you enter the woods
Of a summer evening late,
When the night-air cools on the trout-ringed pools
Where the otter whistles his mate
(They fear not men in the woods,
Because they see so few)

You will hear the beat of a horse's feet,
And the swish of a skirt in the dew,
Steadily cantering through
The misty solitudes,
As though they perfectly knew
The old lost road through the woods…
But there is no road through the woods.

Rudyard Kipling

27

Have You Met A *Wolf*?

A white wolf
at night wolf
beneath a moon
so bright wolf
did you have a fright wolf?

Have you met a wolf?

A grey wolf
a stray wolf
half-way through
the day wolf
did you run away wolf?

Have you met a wolf?

A brown wolf
a proud wolf
letting out
a growl wolf
did you hear it howwwl wolf?

Have you met a wolf?

A green wolf
a lean wolf
looking wild
and mean wolf
was it just a dream wolf?

Have you ever
  maybe never
    try remember…
      *have you met **a wolf**?*

James Carter

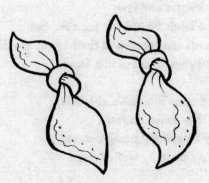

83

*Now here's a challenge. It's got a lovely rhythm.
And it's not too difficult to learn. You might like to
ask your audience to join in the choruses.*

The Jumblies

They went to sea in a Sieve, they did,
 In a Sieve they went to sea:
In spite of all their friends could say,
On a winter's morn, on a stormy day,
 In a Sieve they went to sea!
And when the Sieve turned round and round,
And every one cried, 'You'll all be drowned!'
They called aloud, 'Our Sieve ain't big,
But we don't care a button! we don't care a fig!
 In a Sieve we'll go to sea!'
  Far and few, far and few,
    Are the lands where the Jumblies live;
   Their heads are green, and their hands are blue,
      And they went to sea in a Sieve.

They sailed away in a Sieve, they did,
In a Sieve they sailed so fast,
 With only a beautiful pea-green veil
Tied with a riband by way of a sail,

To a small tobacco-pipe mast;
And every one said, who saw them go,
'O won't they be soon upset, you know!
For the sky is dark, and the voyage is long,
And happen what may, it's extremely wrong
 In a Sieve to sail so fast!'
  Far and few, far and few,
    Are the lands where the Jumblies live;
   Their heads are green, and their hands are blue,
      And they went to sea in a Sieve.

The water it soon came in, it did,
 The water it soon came in;
So to keep them dry, they wrapped their feet
In a pinky paper all folded neat,
 And they fastened it down with a pin.
And they passed the night in a crockery-jar,
And each of them said, 'How wise we are!
Though the sky be dark, and the voyage be long,
Yet we never can think we were rash or wrong,
While round in our Sieve we spin!'
  Far and few, far and few,
    Are the lands where the Jumblies live;
   Their heads are green, and their hands are blue,
      And they went to sea in a Sieve.

And all night long they sailed away;
 And when the sun went down,

They whistled and warbled a moony song
To the echoing sound of a coppery gong,
 In the shade of the mountains brown.
'O Timballo! How happy we are,
When we live in a Sieve and a crockery-jar,
And all night long in the moonlight pale,
We sail away with a pea-green sail,
 In the shade of the mountains brown!'
  Far and few, far and few,
    Are the lands where the Jumblies live;
  Their heads are green, and their hands are blue,
    And they went to sea in a Sieve.

They sailed to the Western Sea, they did,
 To a land all covered with trees,
And they bought an Owl, and a useful Cart,
And a pound of Rice, and a Cranberry Tart,
 And a hive of silvery Bees.
And they bought a Pig, and some green Jack-daws,
And a lovely Monkey with lollipop paws,
And forty bottles of Ring-Bo-Ree,
And no end of Stilton Cheese.
  Far and few, far and few,
    Are the lands where the Jumblies live;
  Their heads are green, and their hands are blue,
    And they went to sea in a Sieve.

And in twenty years they all came back,
 In twenty years or more,
And every one said, 'How tall they've grown!
For they've been to the Lakes, and the Torrible Zone,
 And the hills of the Chankly Bore!'
And they drank their health, and gave them a feast
Of dumplings made of beautiful yeast;
And every one said, 'If we only live,
We too will go to sea in a Sieve,—
To the hills of the Chankly Bore!'
  Far and few, far and few,
    Are the lands where the Jumblies live;
  Their heads are green, and their hands are blue,
    And they went to sea in a Sieve.

Edward Lear

Tips for Learning by Heart and Performing

This section is for parents, carers or teachers who would like to help their children learn poems off by heart.

Learning poems to say or perform aloud, whether to Grandma or to a whole school assembly, can be a great confidence builder for a child, not to mention fun for everyone concerned. It's important with all children, and especially with younger children, to make the experience a happy one. What is crucial is encouraging (and enjoying) youngsters learning and reading poems off by heart. Don't set the bar too high and expect perfection. Timing, expression... these things come with experience.

Make Learning Fun

Some young children enjoy learning poems and songs by heart and do it quite naturally without any help from adults, while others can find it more difficult. Many adults, myself included, find memorising poems and the words to songs a real challenge. But there are techniques that can help.

I often meet adults who enjoy poetry and some who take pride in still being able to recite the poems that they learnt as children. But I also meet many who are bored with, have no interest in, or actively dislike poetry. Further investigation usually reveals that they had a bad time with poetry when they were at school.

So the first rule when teaching or sharing poetry must be to make it FUN. The rule of thumb is to let a child find and choose the poem he or she wants to memorise. If you don't like a poem, why would you want to remember it?

The poems and verses in this book are arranged in order of increasing length (the number of lines is given at the top of each page) and very roughly in order of difficulty. Don't forget that some shorter poems are more complex and harder to learn than long but simple ones.

How To Learn Poems

Current research into learning suggests that the two most effective ways to learn are, firstly, to space learning over a period of time – not to try and learn a whole poem in one go – and, secondly, to test yourself as you go along.

So it makes sense, with the longer poems towards the back of the book, to break them up into chunks. Maybe learn one verse at a time. Or learn the lines in pairs. And do this over several days. Maybe learn a verse a day.

And, when learning poems, say the words out loud. Don't just read them in your head. Read a line, then cover or move the text, and say the line without looking. Here you can help the child by asking them to read aloud, without looking, as they learn.

Francis Bacon had the right idea when he said, in 1620:

If you read a piece of text through twenty times, you will not read it so easily as if you read it ten times while attempting to recite from time to time and consulting the text when your memory fails.

Tips for Memorisation

Repetition

In very simple terms, in order to remember something, our brain creates pathways between neurons. We strengthen those pathways by repeating what we want to learn. The more something is repeated, the stronger the memory becomes.

Choose a repetitive poem!

Sometimes, a poem features a single line, or a verse, that is repeated. If a poem has lots of identical lines there are fewer words to learn. In Colin McNaughton's 'The Crocodile's Brushing His Teeth' (p.23), one line sets up the next line. A poem can be quite long but quite easy to learn because it uses repetition in this way.

Spaced Repetition

Memories become stronger the more you retrieve them. So the best time to recall and repeat something that you wish to learn is just before you are about to forget it! You work to remember it, and that makes the memory stronger.

If you want to make sure you really know the poem by heart, don't try to learn it in one go, but keep coming back to it, waiting for longer between each time. First repeat it after a few minutes, then after a few hours, then a day, then a few days. By that time it really will be stuck in your mind! This is known as spaced repetition.

Rhyme

Verses and poems that rhyme are generally easier to remember than those that don't. In the days before newspapers, when news was shared by troubadours and balladeers touring the country, factual stories would be turned into verses and made to rhyme, simply to make them easier to remember. In 'The Crocodile's Brushing His Teeth' (p.23), once a child has mastered 'The Crocodile's brushing his teeth, I'm afraid', all they have to remember are the rhyming words 'weight', 'late', 'bore' and 'class four'.

That doesn't mean that non-rhyming poems are impossible to learn. Some, in fact, can be just as easy. You just have one less tool – rhyme – to help, that's all.

Rhythm

Probably the most important element of a poem is its rhythm. A strong rhythm can help when you are trying to learn the words. For example, whether the poem is in iambic pentameter or is a limerick, the meter can help you be sure you have it right, or at least anchor the words you can remember.

Being aware of the metrical composition can really help – especially for older children. I'm always aware that over-analysing a poem can kill its enjoyment, so tread carefully here, especially with younger children. But for many, looking closely at a poem, at its construction, or what it really means, will make it much easier to memorise.

Sequence of Events

Some poems lead you naturally through a sequence of events. In Celia Warren's 'Gingerbread Man' (p.42). for example, the last line of each verse helps you start the first line of the next:

...said the Gingerbread Man,
I'd rather be made of marzipan.

Marzipan's too soft,
Said the Marzipan Man,
I'd rather be made of strawberry jam.

Strawberry jam's too runny...

Many poems tell a story. Discussing the story and what it means will help a child to remember what words come next, as in 'I Went to the Animal Fair' (p.34).

Lists

Some poems are really lists. (Indeed, this can be a great way to start young children writing poetry.) In 'The Garden Year' by Sara Coleridge (p.82), each two-line verse begins with the next month.

January brings the snow,
Makes our feet and fingers glow.

February brings the rain,
Thaws the frozen lake again.

What happens in the months, which are listed chronologically, relates directly to the season. And each verse features a rhyme. So although the poem is twenty-four lines long, children find it quite easy to remember.

Making Pictures

Pictures and images can be very helpful when memorising a poem. This only works if the poem lends itself to pictures – otherwise you end up spending all your time thinking of images rather than actually learning the poem – which is not very effective. But many poems do form pictures in our heads.

In Jane Clarke's poem 'Snow' (p.55) for example, we 'see' the snow falling in the first verse, then the settled snow and what the children do with it, and then the old, slushy snow. By being conscious of this process – making yourself aware of the poet's 'painting' – you create a mental movie that will help you remember the poem.

'What Is Pink' by Christina Rossetti (p.53) is also a list poem. But the colours – pink, red, blue, white, yellow, green, violet and orange – are not listed in any obvious order, unlike the months of 'The Garden Year'. So it's trickier to learn. But here we can use the pictures in the poem to help.

Encourage children to imagine the colours of 'What Is Pink'. Take time to build a picture of a garden path made of pink stone. Walk along the path towards an archway of red roses, look up and see the sky is blue... and so on. This technique works very well for longer or more difficult poems.

A *more advanced picture technique*

This is great for older children. First ask the child to think of a familiar place – such as their home. For my poem 'I Am A Princess' (p.59), for example, you could imagine the first verse beginning as you walk towards the door of your home. The door opens. There is the princess. She says she is pleased to meet you but if you come in you must obey lots of rules. Step into the hall, picture it as it is, then imagine the princess there, explaining that you have to bow and curtsey. Do those actions. Then move into the kitchen, where you are told not to argue. Move around your home, making the pictures in your head as strange as you can – this helps you remember. When recalling the poem, the familiarity of the path through the house guides you through the poem.

I once used this technique with amazing success with a class of 35 pupils, each with a different poem to learn for a performance to the school and parents. It does take time though – so use it with care. For a short poem it would be counter-effective.

Understanding

As I've said, understanding a poem can be a help to memorising it. For one thing it's hard to recite a poem with conviction, or meaning, and to 'bring it to life' (see the next section) if you don't actually know what it means. If the child doesn't understand the poem, how will his or her audience?

In 'At the Zoo' (p.21), for example, the poem is easier to picture and remember when you know that 'the grey wolf, with mutton in his maw' means that the wolf has a chunk of meat in his mouth.

And in 'The Jumblies' (p.88), knowing what Ring-Bo-Ree is – as in the line 'forty bottles of Ring-Bo-Ree' – will certainly help, both to remember and to recite the poem. It's a made-up word so why not discuss what it could be? It sounds like it might be something you are not allowed to have until you are grown up. And so it could be recited in a 'I'm not really supposed to know about this' way – almost with a wink. Similarly with the hills of the Chankly Bore. Chankly Bore sounds as if it could be quite a scary place. Especially if it's in the Torrible Zone!

Bring a poem to life with performance

Having learnt a poem off by heart, it's great to perform it, maybe for family or friends, maybe at school – for the class or in assembly. Performing a poem can be much more than simply saying it out loud. There are lots of ways to make it more fun and more interesting.

Actions

They say actions speak louder than words, but that's not always the case. When I judged the BBC's Off by Heart competition it seemed that every teacher had encouraged their charges to accompany each poem with exaggerated gestures which were meant to enhance the poem. This actually did the opposite for me: I was so entranced by some of the weird gesticulations that I missed many of the words being spoken.

Actions are good – research shows that we take in more information when someone accompanies what they are saying with hand gestures, and they can also help the reciter's memory. But less is more: don't overdo it.

Volume

If you've ever coached children for a performance you may have found yourself, as I have, continually telling them to speak louder and to make their pronunciation clearer. In school, it's always good for the teacher to stand at the back. You can cup your ears to indicate if the child isn't loud enough. If they are nervous they could imagine that they are saying the poem just to you. Ask them to look at you, and only you, as they concentrate on their task.

But sometimes a soft voice is appropriate. And sometimes the volume and tone of a voice needs to vary as the poem is recited. Make sure the child understands the meaning of the poem, and they will find it easier to understand which parts should be loud and which quiet.

In a public performance, encourage them to say the poem loudly enough – a live audience can be a bit scary – and to imagine they are saying the poem to someone at the back of the room.

And remember, a poem that a child doesn't really understand will likely be incomprehensible to the hearer.

Accents

For older children, reading a poem in a different accent can be fun. It's probably best to keep this to comic poems, especially if the child isn't that good at the accent.

Some poems are written in an accent – by Caribbean poets like Grace Nichols, or Scottish poets like Robert Burns, for example. If the child can 'do' the accent that's fine. But if he or she can't, it's probably best to recite it in his or her normal voice – or it may well sound peculiar!

Pace

Children tend to recite too fast. But don't go too far the other way and make them recite too slowly, either. You will know that listening to a long poem or story read in a dull, slow monotone quickly sends you to sleep. Or into the realm of daydream. We assimilate information better if it's delivered reasonably quickly, as long as the words are said clearly.

Varying the pace of a longer poem keeps the listener's interest, as does the use of a dramatic pause – a favourite ploy of teachers to keep children on the ball in assemblies! Reading a poem with a strong rhythm or meter is great fun. But be careful that the rhythm doesn't carry the reader away.

Similarly, a slow poem written in iambic meter (di dum di dum di dum di dum) can easily become very plodding and tiresome to listen to.

For older children, it might be worth playing them a recording of poetry so that they can hear what a poem sounds like when read by an actor or by its author. The online Poetry Archive is an excellent source for this.

Starting and Ending

Encourage children to wait until the audience is ready before they start to recite a poem. Show them how to first announce the title of the piece and the name of the author, followed by a pause. Then they can begin.

Similarly, at the end of a poem, tell them never to rush. Children often gabble the last couple of lines and even turn away as they deliver them, in their anxiety to be finished. Stress that they should actually slow down towards the end, deliver the final lines clearly and firmly, and then wait a second or two before leaving the 'stage'.

Practice!

It is usually necessary to read a poem many times to learn it off by heart. Once it is learned, it becomes much easier to perform. Similarly a performance improves with practice. So if there is to be a public performance, have plenty of rehearsals. Let the child practise where the performance will be – on the stage, or at the front of the school hall. Although there's not a lot to be done if the child has stage fright, practice can guard against this: it stands to reason that, once a poem is completely memorised, and once its performance has been rehearsed enough, the child will feel more much more confident 'on the night'.

Other Ideas

If you are a teacher, you might try asking your class for ideas about how they feel they could best perform a poem. I tried this with a class I was running a workshop for and we came up with about a dozen ideas – including dressing up, using puppets, performing in twos or threes or larger groups and having musical accompaniment.

Invite a poet into your school or class. There's nothing like hearing and watching a real poet perform and read his or her poems to inspire and motivate a class.

I've given you lots of ideas and tips to help your children, whether they are family or a class at school, how to learn and to perform poems. But remember, especially with young children, don't overload them with all the things they should be doing. If they are enjoying the process they will do well, become more confident, and come back for more. So I'll end as I began, by urging you to remember – make it FUN!

24

Goodbye Rhyme!

We're ready now
it's time to say
we've tidied up
we've cleared away

We've done our work
been out to play
we've learnt a lot
in just a day

We read a book
we talked, we sang
and in PE
we hopped, we ran

We looked for bugs
we caught a few
we watched them crawl
we drew them too

Louise (Billy)   Wed / Sat

Shire Horse Centre
Thurs, Fri, Sun

Tabitha   Mon / Sat / Sun

Mannington Gardens 11 - 5pm
Boardwalk every day

Zara ④   Sheringham Park   Pensthorpe

Zara / Charlotte   Felbrigg   Redwings
10.30 - 4
Fri, Sat
Sun, Mon
pre book

~~Dippy~~ Treehouse

Jacob & Harvey

~~Lego dinos~~

Ellis   The Links

Millipedes   Mish Mash   Rabbits.
200

Eliza   East Raynham
trail
Mon - Fri
Plantation garden &

Zara   Catherine   UEA gym   Nathex
10.30
- 2.30

Eira & Erin   Choc workshop

Piano lamp

Underidewd
Duncan + Jean

RAF Air Defence Museum Tues-Sat
(10-5pm)

We're in our coats
and here we're sat
we're all together
on the mat

So now we've done
our goodbye rhyme
we'll all stand up...
it's homeward time!

James Carter

Acknowledgements and Copyrights

'A Poem That, Despite Being Only One Word Long...', 'Animal Sneezes', 'Chicken Soup', 'A Silver Birch', 'Ways to Come to School', 'There Are No Such Things as Monsters!!!', 'Pirate Hat' © Roger Stevens.

'Chocolate in the House' © Andy Seed 2010, from *Razzle Dazzle* (Hands Up Books).

'Fat Cat' © Roger Stevens, first published in *I Did Not Eat the Goldfish* (Macmillan Children's Books 2002).

'Gingerbread Man' © Celia Warren. First published in *Food Rhymes (First Verses)* edited by John Foster, OUP, 1998.

'Hey Diddle Diddle' © Roger Stevens, first published in *On My Way to School I Saw a Dinosaur* (A&C Black 2005).

'I Am a Princess' © Roger Stevens, first published in *A First Poetry Book* edited by Pie Corbett and Gaby Morgan (Macmillan Children's Books 2012).

'Ladybird' © Brian D'Arcy, 2013, reprinted by permission of the author.

'Like Grandad' from *Celebration* by Joan Poulson, UNICEF (1993), by permission of the author.

'My Little Pet Cattery' © John Rice, by permission of the author.